This book belongs to

....

....

Useful words

(in the order they appear in this book)

books

car

town

frames

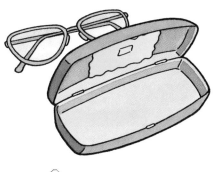

glasses case

school

teacher

house

Grey letters represent silent letters.

Golden Girl's Glasses

Julie McLaren

Golden Girl had to go for an eye test because the words in her books did not seem very clear. She did not want to go.

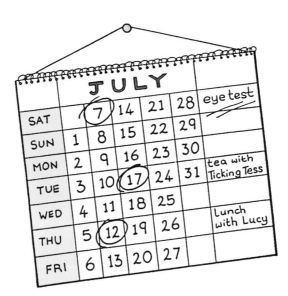

"Don't worry, it won't hurt," said Clever Cat. "Come on, you can come with me."

They got into Clever Cat's car and went into town.

Clever Cat and Golden Girl got there just in time. Golden Girl had to look through some funny glasses and read some letters. Then she chose some green frames.

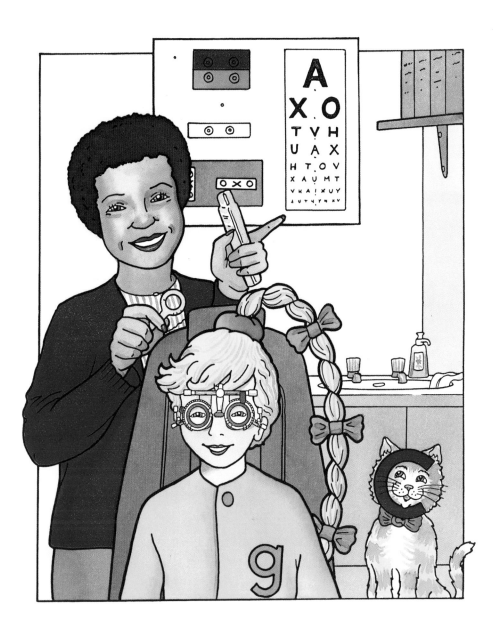

When her glasses were ready
Golden Girl went to collect them.
She put them away in their case.

"I'll wear them later," she said.

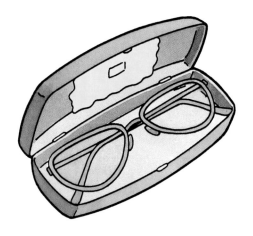

On Monday, Golden Girl went to school.

"Where are your glasses?" asked her teacher.

"I'll wear them tomorrow," said Golden Girl.

Later, Golden Girl went to Maxine's house to play. They were playing 'school' and Golden Girl was the teacher. She held her book very close to her face.

"Where are your new glasses?" asked Maxine.

Golden Girl had left them at home. She did not want to wear her glasses.

Golden Girl's gran was cleaning the bedrooms. She found Golden Girl's glasses under her bed.

"What are these doing here?" she wondered.

Just then, Golden Girl came home.
Her gran asked her about the
glasses. Golden Girl began to cry.

"All my friends will laugh at me,"
she sobbed.

Golden Girl's gran went to find Clever Cat. Clever Cat gave her lots of pictures to show Golden Girl. They were pictures of famous people wearing glasses..

Golden Girl liked the pictures, so she took her glasses to school the next day. But she was still a little shy.

When she got out her reading book, Golden Girl put her glasses on.

"You look great in your glasses," said all her friends.

"And your reading is much better, too!" said her teacher.

The Letterlanders

 Annie Apple

 Bouncy Ben

 Clever Cat

 Dippy Duck

 Eddy Elephant

 Fireman Fred

Golden Girl

 **Hairy Hat Man**

 Impy Ink

 Jumping Jim

 Kicking King

 Lucy Lamp Lady

 Munching Mike

 Naughty Nick

 Oscar Orange

 Poor Peter

 Quarrelsome Queen

 Robber Red

 Sammy Snake

 Ticking Tess

 Uppy Umbrella

 Vase of Violets

 Wicked Water Witch

 Max and Maxine

 Yellow Yo-yo Man

 Zig Zag Zebra

This edition produced for
The Book People Ltd., Hall Wood Avenue,
Haydock, St. Helens WA11 9UL

Published by Collins Educational
An imprint of HarperCollins*Publishers* Ltd
77-85 Fulham Palace Road
London W6 8JB

The HarperCollins website address is
www.**fire**and**water**.com

First published 1999

ISBN 0 00 303438 0

LETTERLAND® is a registered trademark of Lyn Wendon.

British Library Cataloguing in Publication Data
A catalogue record for this book is available from the British Library.

Acknowledgement
The publishers would like to acknowledge with thanks the help provided by
Naved Ashraf BSc (Hons), MCOptom. of Vision Express.

Written by Julie McLaren
Illustrated by Jan West
Colouring by Gina Hart
Designed by Michael Sturley
Consultant: Lyn Wendon, originator of Letterland

Printed by Printing Express, Hong Kong